Busy Time

Naomi!

Kemi!

Beth!

Jen!

Hello!

Welcome to our Milkshake! make and do activity book!

If you want to make something special there are lots of activities in this book that you will really enjoy.

For some of the activities you might need a little bit of help from a grown-up!

Come and join us for lots of make-and-do fun!

Love from Naomi x Kemi x Beth x Jen x

Enchanted Secret Garden

Make your own magical miniature garden from natural materials you can find on a walk.

Things you will need:
- A shallow tray or dish
- Tin foil
- Moss or grass
- Small stones
- Twigs
- Pine cones
- Toy animals
- Flowers
- Leaves
- Cress seeds (optional)

1.
Put the folded tin foil in the centre of the tray. This will be your beautiful shimmering lake.

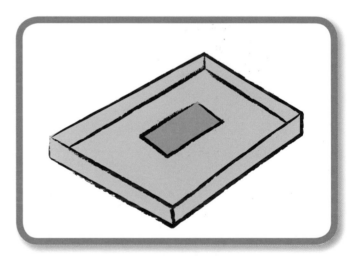

2.
Cover your tray with moss, but make sure you can still see your lake! The moss is your grass and hills!

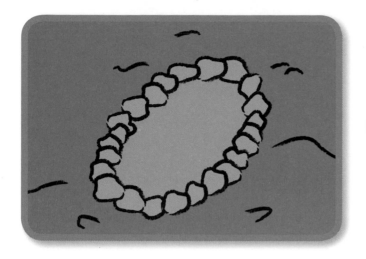

3.

Put the stones around the edge of the lake to give it a border.

4.

Arrange the twigs and pine cones on the moss and between the hills to look like trees and bushes.

5.

Now decorate your garden by placing your toy animals, flowers and leaves in it. You have made a truly magical woodland garden.

What a wonderful garden!

6.

If you have cress seeds, sprinkle them on to the garden to give it real plants. Don't forget you'll need to water them!

Whizz! Bang! Sparkle!

It's time to celebrate! Make a Whizz! Bang! Sparkle! picture and have a firework display in your own home!

Things you will need:
• **Paper** • **Wax crayons** • **Black paint** • **Paintbrush**

1.

Draw this picture of a firework on your paper using your favourite coloured crayons. Make sure all the lines shoot out of the same point!

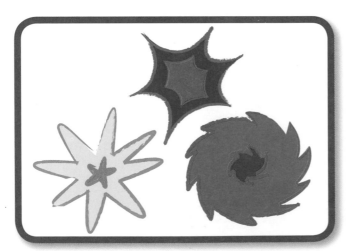

2.

Here are some other pictures of fireworks. Draw some of them with your crayons too.

3.

Fill your whole page with fireworks! Use lots of different colours. Can you make up some of your own fireworks for your picture?

4.

Now cover your whole picture with black paint! Make sure you get paint on every bit of paper. Watch the fireworks appear in the night sky!

5.

Wait for your picture to dry. Now decide where in your house you want your magical firework display to be!

Wow, it looks like a real firework display. Light 'em up!

Scary Tiger Mask

This exciting mask will make you look fierce!

Things you will need:
- Tracing Paper • Pencil • Card • Scissors
- Colouring pens, crayons or paints • Sticky tape
- A piece of elastic or a strip of paper

Don't Forget!

Ask a grown-up for help when you are using scissors!

1.

Trace the tiger's face on to a piece of card and then carefully cut it out.

2.

Hold the mask up to your face to check it fits! Then cut holes for the tiger's eyes. Make sure they are in the right place!

3.

Now colour in your tiger's face. Use your colouring pens, crayons or paints to make it look really fierce! Try to stay inside the lines and colour in all its markings!

m is for milkshake!

4.

Attach the elastic or the strip of paper to both sides of the back of the mask using sticky tape.

5.

Now practise your roar!

7

Yummy Scrummy Smoothie!

Jen's delicious fruity smoothie is perfect as a tasty snack – and even better shared with a friend!

Things you will need: • A blender • 2 glasses • 2 straws • A mango (chopped into cubes) • A chopped banana • 500ml orange juice

Don't Forget!

Ask a grown-up to help you chop the mango and the banana!

1.
Put your chopped mango into the blender.

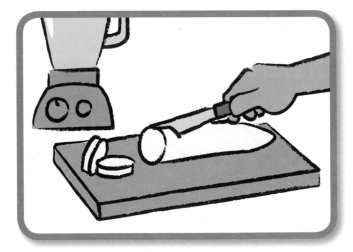

2.
Put the banana into the blender.

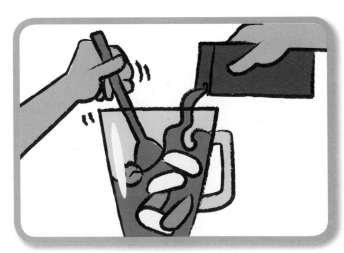

3.
Pour the orange juice on top of the other fruit.

4.

Ask a grown-up to help you, and switch the blender on for ten seconds. Whizz until the mixture is smooth and looking delicious!

5.

Pour the smoothie into two glasses, ready to share with a friend!

6.

Don't forget to top them off with colourful straws!

That looks like a really delicious smoothie!

Seaside Search

It's a sunny day and everyone has gone to the seaside. Can you spot all the things listed below? Put a tick next to each thing as you spot it.

Bucket ☐   Rubber Ring ☐   Sandcastle ☐   Picnic Basket ☐   Flowery Swimsuit ☐

Ice Cream ☐   Sun Hat ☐   Grandad's Toes ☐   Beach Towel ☐   Seagull ☐

Now colour the picture in.

Mix-Up!

Oh no! The animals are all hungry
and their food has got mixed up! Can you draw
lines to match each animal with its dinner?
Some are on your stickers page!

Did you find them all?
Well done!
Give yourself a shiny gold star!

Rhyme Time

Little Princess loves to sing, but some of the words are missing from these songs! Can you help her finish them? Decorate the pictures with your stickers. Then sing the songs out loud!

Hey diddle diddle,

The cat and the fiddle,

The cow jumped over the moon,

The little dog laughed to see such fun,

And the dish ran away with the spoon.

Humpty Dumpty sat on a wall.

Humpty Dumpty had a great fall.

All the King's horses,

And all the King's men,

Couldn't put Humpty together again.

Naomi!

Kemi!

Mary, Mary, quite contrary,
How does your garden grow?
With silver bells and cockle shells,
And pretty maids all in a row.

Pat-a-cake, pat-a-cake,
Baker's man!
Bake me a cake,
As fast as you can.

Pat it, and prick it,
And mark it with a B,
And put it in the oven,
For Baby and me.

Now I can sing
all my favourite songs!

Colouring Crazy

It's party time! Grab your best crayons and use your stickers to colour in this picture.

Farmyard Fun

It's busy on the farm today!
Look at all the animals with the farmer.

How many of each animal can you find?

____	____	____	____	____
ducks	pigs	**dogs**	**horses**	sheep

Cress Caterpillars

A wiggly way to watch your own seeds grow!
You'll need to be patient though – once you've
planted your caterpillar's fur it takes about
a week for it to grow!

Things you will need: • Half an egg box
• Pens, pencils, paint or stickers for decoration
• Cotton wool • Cress seeds • Bowl of water

Don't Forget!

Ask a grown-up for help
when you are using scissors!

1.

Cut an egg box in half.

2.

Now you can decorate your egg
box. Make it look like a caterpillar
by adding the eyes from the sticker
page! Now paint your caterpillar.
What colour is it going to be?

3.
Make your cotton wool damp by dipping it in some water. Don't make it too wet or your caterpillar will be a soggy mess!

4.
Place the damp cotton wool in the caterpillar, so that it covers the bottom of the egg box.

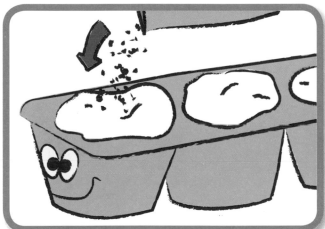

5.
Sprinkle cress seeds all over the damp cotton wool. Make sure all the cotton wool is covered in cress seeds.

6.
Keep the cotton wool damp and wait for your cress to grow to make your caterpillar's furry body!

Beautiful Butterflies

Butterflies are symmetrical. That means both sides are exactly the same! When you have finished your picture, hold a mirror along the middle to reflect one wing. Is the picture still the same?

Things you will need:
• **Paper** • **Paints** • **Pencil** • **Paintbrush**

1.

Fold your piece of paper in half.

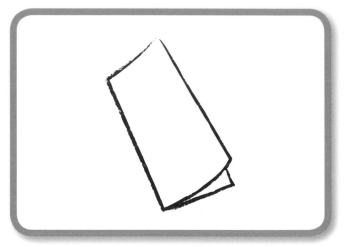

2.

Open the piece of paper out and trace the half-butterfly shape.

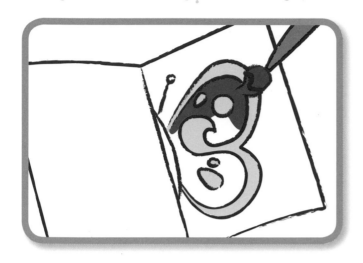

3.

Paint inside the shape using lots of different colours. See how many different patterns you can paint, and how many different colours you can use!

4.

Fold your paper in half again. Press it down firmly so that the paint sticks to both sides.

5.

Open out your paper to see your beautiful butterfly!

**Well done!
What a lovely butterfly!**

Pen Pot Pal

This friendly elephant will help you remember to keep all your pens and pencils tidy!

Things you will need:
- A small flowerpot • Paper • Scissors • Glue or sticky tape
- A pencil • Colouring pens, pencils or paints

1.
Cut a piece of paper big enough to go around the outside of your flowerpot. Stick it to the flowerpot.

2.
Cut a thin strip of paper for the trunk. Wrap this piece around a pencil so it has a slight curl. Then stick it to the front of your flowerpot, about halfway up.

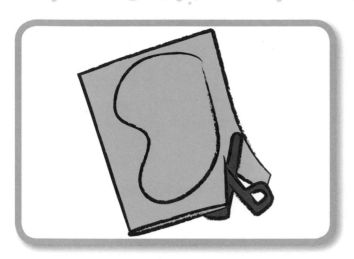

3.

Fold a piece of paper in half. Draw an ear shape on one half and then cut it out around the shape through both pieces of paper.

4.

When you unfold the paper you will have two ear shapes! Stick the ears on either side of the flowerpot.

5.

Use the eyes from the sticker sheet to put on your elephant. These should go above the trunk.

6.

Use your colouring pens, pencils or paints to decorate your elephant. You could give him tusks, wrinkles and even some hair!

Dangling Dinos

Make some dinosaurs just like Harry and His Bucket Full of Dinosaurs! They can hang in your window and will move with the breeze.

Things you will need: • Tracing paper • Scissors • Card • Pencil • Coloured pencils, pens or paints • String • Sticky tape • Coat hanger

Don't Forget!

Ask a grown-up for help when you are using scissors!

1.

Trace around the pictures of the dinosaurs with your tracing paper and put them on some card. Cut the pictures out and colour the dinosaurs in.

2.

Attach a piece of string to the top of each of your animals with sticky tape.

3.

Tie the other ends of the string to the coat hanger. You can use sticky tape if you find knots a bit difficult!

Wow! My dinosaurs really move!

Milkshake! Mobile

Now you can make a Milkshake! mobile. Use the stickers of Kemi, Jen, Beth and Naomi on the sticker page. Stick them onto card and carefully cut round them.

Kemi!

Jen!

Naomi!

Beth!

Don't Forget!
Ask a grown-up for help when you are using scissors!

24